TALES FROM THE PITCH

MO SALAH

HARRY CONINX

RAVEN

For Sharu, to inspire you at the next Stros

CONTENTS

I

HAT-TRICK HERO

October 2021, Old Trafford, Manchester, England
Manchester United v Liverpool

"So what is it, then? Nine games in a row you're on?" Roberto Firmino asked, nudging Mohamed.

"Yeah, that's right," Mo smiled.

The Liverpool players were sitting in the dressing room at Old Trafford, home of their arch-rivals, Man United.

It was still early in the new season, but this game was

already crucial. Chelsea and Man City had both started the season in brutally good form, and it was essential that Liverpool win this game, just to keep pace with them.

"What do we think then, guys?" Virgil van Dijk asked, leaning over into their conversation. "The United team. How are they going to play?"

"Are you worried about going up against Ronaldo?" Firmino asked. "Last time we played him, we lost a Champions League final."

"That was a long time ago." Virgil frowned, clearly objecting to being reminded about that defeat.

Mo flinched, thinking back to that final in 2018, when he'd had to go off in the first half with an injury that had almost ruled him out of the World Cup.

Liverpool had gone on to win the Champions League the next year, and then the Premier League the year after, but Mo still regretted that first final. It hadn't been Ronaldo that day – it had been Gareth Bale, who had won it for Madrid. But now they were facing off against him again.

"It doesn't matter about Ronaldo anyway," Virgil

insisted. "We've got Mo. He's scored every time we've come here."

"Yeah, but that doesn't matter," Mo laughed. "It's not about me scoring – it's about beating *them*."

Any goals Mo scored on the way to getting the win today would be a bonus. But he also knew that, if he did score today, he'd have scored in every one of his last ten games.

Mo wouldn't admit this to the rest of the players, but he saw today as an opportunity for him to take on Ronaldo, to prove himself as the best player in the world right now. If he added a couple of goals today and helped Liverpool to a huge win, then that wouldn't hurt his case one bit.

"Are we ready then, boys?" Jürgen Klopp said, silencing the chatter in the room. "We've played these boys a lot over the years. They've got a few new signings, but we know what we can do."

"High pressure, high intensity from the start, lads," Jordan Henderson added. "Get the ball to our wide guys, get support to them."

"I know it's early, but the title is on the line here,

lads," James Milner said. "I've played for teams who've lost the title in October because they fell too far behind."

Walking out onto the pitch, Mo glanced over at United's defenders, who were all looking at him nervously. This game was far more important to Man U than it was to Liverpool.

"We make a quick start and we silence the fans," Henderson nodded to Mo. "Don't be scared to shoot early, panic them."

"But don't forget about me back here!" Trent Alexander-Arnold added. "I'll need you tracking back, give me a bit of support."

Mo laughed, but he agreed with Trent. Klopp's style of play had been successful because the players all worked for each other. It was exhausting, but if everyone pulled their weight, they knew it would get them results.

In the first few minutes, Andy Robertson passed inside to Firmino. The Brazilian flicked the ball in behind the defence to Mo, and suddenly there was only one defender between him and the goal.

"Mo! Now!" Naby Keïta shouted, as he sprinted past Mo's right shoulder. Mo timed his pass to perfection, so that Keïta stayed onside. The Guinean midfielder took one touch and slid the ball past David de Gea, giving Liverpool the lead.

They had made the perfect start.

"Naby, lad!" Mo shouted, jumping on the goalscorer's back, happy to get an assist.

Diogo Jota soon doubled Liverpool's lead, after diverting home an Alexander-Arnold cross.

"We've got two – and Mo's not even scored yet!" Trent laughed, as they celebrated. "Someone get him the ball!"

Twenty minutes later, the ball hobbled around on the edge of the box, eventually falling at the feet of Naby Keïta, who was running in from the right-hand side.

"Now!" Mo called, sprinting ahead of his marker, Maguire, and getting to the near post first.

He met the ball with his weaker right foot, whipping it into the top corner. De Gea could do nothing about it.

"That's ten!" Roberto Firmino yelled, leaping onto Mo's back. "Ten in a row!"

Mo grinned as he punched the air in front of the jeering United fans.

It didn't take long for Mo to get his second, and it came before half-time. Once again, United were opened up far too easily and Diogo Jota found himself in the box. Mo was lurking on the right-hand side, completely unmarked and open.

"Diogo!" he called. "I'm free!"

It was a simple pass for Jota to find Mo and, with Luke Shaw closing him down, he struck it first-time, drilling it towards the near post. De Gea dived, but he was too slow and the ball nestled in the back of the net.

Mo didn't even celebrate this time, just pumping his fists where he stood and looking up to the sky.

4-0!

United held out into half-time, but early in the second half Mo completed his hat-trick. Jordan Henderson threaded a ball through and Mo raced clear, sprinting away from the United defence. De Gea came out to close him down, but Mo had finished from this position a thousand times in his career, and he dinked the ball over the onrushing keeper.

Liverpool had five and Mo had three of them! He had a hat-trick at Old Trafford.

"I can't remember the last time someone came here and scored a hat-trick," Jordan Henderson grinned, embracing Mo.

"Not since Brazilian Ronaldo in 2003," Andy Robertson added.

"Not bad company," Mo shrugged.

Now 5-0 up, Liverpool could lift the pressure a little. They had a lot of games coming up, so were happy to take it easier, avoiding risking any injuries.

The rest of the match was uneventful, but the damage had already been done. Liverpool had battered United and sent out a message to the rest of the football world. They were back – and they were here to reclaim their title.

Mo had sent out his own message too. He'd already won the Golden Boot, the Champions League and the Premier League. Now he was telling anybody who was listening that he wasn't done.

He wanted to become the best player in the world.

And, with a hat-trick against United, showing up Cristiano Ronaldo in his own stadium, he was well on his way to proving that.

2
BIG DREAMS

June 2002, Nagrig, Basyoun, Egypt

"Come on, Mo! Come out and play!" The voice of Mo's little brother, Nasr, echoed around their small house.

"Not now, Nasr!" Mo groaned. Normally, he'd be desperate to go outside and play football, even if it was just with his little brother, but things were different today. One of his idols, Italian striker Francesco Totti, was playing in the World Cup.

Mo's eyes were fixed on the small TV screen in their living room, as the national anthems rang out of the small speaker.

"Are you sure you don't want to play with your brother?" his mum asked, sitting down next to him. "It's a beautiful day outside. The other kids will join in if they see you out there."

"At half-time, maybe," he insisted, but she gave him one of those looks.

"Muuum!" he complained. "It's Totti. He's my hero."

"I thought Ronaldo was your hero," she laughed. "You spent your whole birthday talking about how you were going to play for Barcelona and Inter, just like him."

"Well yeah, he's my hero too," Mo shrugged. "And Zidane. I have a few – but it's only Totti playing today. Anyway, I don't want to play for Barcelona any more. Ronaldo is going to Real Madrid, so I want to play for them."

"Real Madrid, huh?" his mum smiled. "That's a long way from Egypt. I hope you'll take us all with you."

"Nope." Mo smiled, folding his arms. "I'm going to

Madrid on my own, and I'm going to have my own big flat-screen TV, so I can watch all the football I want without being disturbed."

"I'm sure you will," his mum laughed, tousling her son's hair. "But, right now, you live in Nagrig, so you still have to do as I say. And I'm telling you to run outside and play with your little brother. Just for 20 minutes. Totti will still be here when you get back."

"But it's the middle of the day!" Mo complained, still not turning to look at his mum. "It's too hot!"

"That's never stopped you before."

"What if Totti scores while I'm gone?"

"If anyone scores, I'll let you know and you can come rushing in. Now go!" She lifted Mo by his armpits and pushed him towards the door.

He stumbled outside, shielding his eyes from the sun, and spotted his brother kicking a ball against the wall.

"Give me the ball!" Mo called, as his brother turned towards him. "Where's the goal?"

Nasr pointed at a couple of T-shirts on the ground, arranged as goalposts, then fed a pass towards Mo, who controlled it with the outside of his left foot and feinted to shoot, then dribbled around a couple of imaginary defenders and blasted a shot towards the goal.

It bounced back off the wall behind the goal and came out towards them.

"Why d'you want to watch the game?" Nasr asked, screwing his eyes up at Mo. "Egypt aren't even playing."

"Egypt aren't at the World Cup," Mo sighed. "We've not been there for years."

"Oh!" Nasr frowned. "Maybe, when we play for them, we can qualify. Then you don't have to watch stupid Italy and Totti."

"It's not stupid," Mo snapped. "Why don't we play one-on-one, me against you? I'll be Totti. You be one of the South Korean defenders."

Mo got the ball and dribbled at his brother, skipping round him easily. But before he could get a shot away, his brother nipped back around him and got the ball back.

"Did Totti lose the ball so easily?" Nasr taunted.

Mo glared at his brother and charged at him, diving into a tackle. They quickly became engaged in a long, hard-fought battle, with both of them scoring, tackling, shoving and pushing each other.

Before long, other kids around the neighbourhood turned up, with Mo assigning them to either "South Korea" or "Italy", depending on who he wanted in his team.

The kick-around quickly broke out into a full-scale game, and the high midday sun that had drenched both sets of players in sweat slowly began to fade. Soon the game was floodlit by the lights in the windows of the surrounding houses.

"How many have you scored, Mo?" his friend, Ramy, asked, during a break in play.

"I have no idea – but more than you!" he teased.

Eventually, everyone collapsed to the floor, exhausted. Nobody really knew who had won, but then nobody really cared.

Mo helped Nasr to his feet, and the pair stumbled back into their house, waving their goodbyes to their friends.

"You two have been gone ages!" his mum exclaimed, as they came in the living room.

Mo spotted the TV and suddenly remembered why he'd been so reluctant to go out and play.

"The match!" he shouted, turning to his mum. "Why didn't you call me? What happened?"

"I did," she replied. "Several times – but you didn't hear me."

"Who won? Did Totti score?"

"South Korea," she said. "And you didn't miss much. Totti was sent off!"

"No way!"

"Yep," she confirmed. "Italy are out, I'm afraid."

Mo shook his head in disbelief.

"At least Ronaldo is still in," Nasr added. "And, one day, we're going to play at the World Cup too, Mum!"

"Really?" his mum chuckled. "Well I hope you do better than Totti did today."

"We will," Mo insisted. "We'll win the whole thing."

3

MOVING FORWARD

November 2006, Nasr City, Cairo, Egypt
Al Mokawloon Academy v ENPPI Academy

"Are you ready for today, Mo?" Mo's friend, Ahmed, said, leaning over and tapping him on the shoulder. "This is the big one."

"Is it?" Mo replied, looking up and suddenly feeling very nervous.

"All the games are big, Mo," Ahmed continued, leaning back in his seat on the train and stretching his legs. "But these are our rivals – and you're playing. It's exciting, right?"

"Is it?" Mo answered vaguely, staring out of the train window. They had already been on the train for an hour, and there was another train after this, then a bus, before they would make it to the ground.

After playing for his village's amateur youth team, Mo had made it into Al Mokawloon's academy in Cairo – the biggest step so far in his fledgling football career.

In fact, it had all been a lucky accident. A scout had turned up to watch a different player in Mo's team, but Mo had impressed the scout so much that he'd decided to sign Mo instead.

Al Mokawloon were one of the biggest clubs in the country, but it had taken a lot of convincing for his parents to let him make the long journey to Cairo every day.

"I need to do this if I'm going to become a professional footballer one day," Mo had insisted.

"Every day, it's going to take four hours to get there and back," his mum had replied.

"I know, but I still want to do it."

Mo was still only 14 years old, but his parents found it too hard to say no to that kind of determination.

Yet, for the last couple of months, it had all felt like a massive mistake. Mo was the fifth-choice left-back in the academy, and he was often played out of position, on the left wing or in centre-midfield. It wasn't the role he'd imagined for himself when he'd agreed to start playing at Al Mokawloon.

But Ahmed was right about today's game. Mo was going to be playing at left-back, the role that he'd been training for since he'd started playing football.

"Come on, you know it's exciting!" Ahmed insisted. "We're going to play together properly for the first time – you at left-back, me on the wing!"

"I know. I'm just nervous," Mo replied. "It's my first proper game, my first real chance to impress."

"You'll be fine, Mo," Ahmed continued. "The only reason you've not been part of the team is because he has to pick those other guys – because he knows their dads."

Mo wasn't so sure. He knew that a lot of favouritism went on in the team, but picking the team based on who people's dads were seemed crazy.

Eventually, their train came to a shuddering halt in Cairo, and they both darted through the station to catch their next train. After that, they had to get a bus to the pitch.

They were late arriving at the ground, and the pre-match warm-up was well underway.

"Mo! Ahmed!" the coach bellowed. "Five laps of the pitch! Get going! You're behind!"

Dumping their bags next to the goal, they set off, jogging around the pitch. After only a couple of laps, it became clear that Mo was finding it easier than Ahmed, so he slowed his pace to match that of his friend.

"You go on, Mo!" Ahmed panted. "You wanted to impress him – this is your opportunity."

Mo nodded and sprinted off, finishing the laps with ease. He'd always been small for his age and, although many coaches considered that to be a weakness, it also made him very quick.

After a brief warm-up with the ball, they were ready for the match to begin. Mo was shaking with nerves, feeling anxious balls of energy wriggling up and down every part of his body.

"You'll be fine!" Ahmed called over, spotting him shivering, despite the heat. "Once you get that first touch of the ball, you'll forget everything else!"

He was right, of course.

Just seconds after the whistle went, the ball was fizzed over to Mo. He controlled it deftly with the inside of his left foot and was instantly looking for a pass, slipping it down the line towards Ahmed.

Suddenly, the nerves were gone. A minute ago, he'd felt sick with worry and anticipation. Now, all he could think about was where he could get space, how he could get the ball, who he was going to pass to.

Despite playing as a left-back – a defender – Mo was keen to get forward and help with the attack whenever he could.

Anyway, Al Mokawloon were the much better side in this game and there wasn't really much defending that needed doing.

After 10 minutes, he exchanged passes with Ahmed and burst through into the box. He was too quick for the first defender, and now he had an opportunity to shoot. He tried to get as much power as he could behind the shot, imagining it rippling the back of the net. But when he looked up, the ball had flown high over the bar.

Mo kicked the air in frustration.

"Head up, Mo. Keep going!" Ahmed shouted.

Not long after, he got another chance, weaving his way through the defenders, but this time his shot was straight at the keeper.

Before half-time, he got a third chance, playing a slick one-two with Ahmed, before racing clear. The keeper came rushing out and Mo flicked the ball around him, but this time he'd made the angle too tight, and his shot cannoned back off the post.

"You're doing everything right, Mo," his coach told him at half-time. "Keep it up and the goals will come."

But in the second half, Mo had two more chances to score, and he missed the target each time.

Al Mokawloon ended up winning the game easily, but Mo was furious with himself.

"I just can't believe I didn't score," he complained to Ahmed. "I was *so* rubbish! How's he ever going to pick me again? How can I ever play again?"

"It's fine, bro," Ahmed insisted. "You're a defender.

Plus, you made most of those chances yourself. You played well."

"Even a defender should score one of those."

Mo could feel the emotions building. He should have scored – it wasn't right that he hadn't. The emotions suddenly bubbled over and tears welled up in his eyes.

He wiped them away as the coach came up to him. The coach's expression was unreadable, but Mo could sense what he was going to say. Mo's time in the first team had been brief, but now it was surely coming to an end.

"I didn't know you could play like that," Coach Mohamed said with a smile. "We've been wasting you in defence all this time."

"The misses … " Mo sniffed, angrily wiping away another tear.

"Oh, don't worry about that!" Mohamed insisted. "We'll work on that. I think we've got a new position for you now. Winger."

Mo looked up at him, confused. "What?"

"Oh, yeah," the coach replied. "And trust me, kid, this time next year, you'll have 30 goals to your name."

4

KINDNESS

September 2008, Nagrig, Basyoun, Egypt

"It's all gone!" Mo heard his dad shout. Mo had just returned home after playing a match in Alexandria. He'd bagged a goal and an assist in the game, so he was in a good mood.

But this sounded like something bad had happened.

"What's going on?" Mo called out, stepping in through the front door.

"We've been robbed! All our savings are gone," his mum replied.

"We all just went for a walk, and we left the door unlocked ... " Nasr added, without looking up at Mo.

At that moment, a police officer appeared in the doorway behind Mo.

"Mr and Mrs Salah?" the officer said, knocking on the open door. "We've found the person responsible – he's down at the police station."

The entire Salah family looked at the police officer and breathed a sigh of relief.

"Would you like to press charges?" the officer asked.

"Of course we would!" Mo's dad replied immediately.

"Do we?" Mo said, quietly.

"Why wouldn't we?" Mo's dad asked. "He stole everything we had!"

"Well, why would the robber do this?" Mo asked, looking up at his dad. "Maybe he doesn't have any money – or a job. We could help him out. I can give him some of the money I've earned from football."

Everyone, including the police officer, looked at Mo with a stunned expression.

Already, at the age of 16, Mo had earned a reputation for kindness. When he'd played for the Amateur Youth Center team, before Al Mokawloon, he'd taken food to the training pitch every day to feed the puppies that lived under the stands surrounding the pitch.

For Mo, it was the obvious thing to do – the puppies needed feeding, and if nobody else was going to do it, he would.

Mo's mum looked at the police officer, then at Mo. "Your heart is so big, Mo," she smiled tearfully. "Maybe we should do as you suggest," she said, turning towards Mo's dad and the police officer.

Mo's dad's face was expressionless as he thought it over, and Mo wasn't sure what he was going to say.

Then he broke into a smile. "Yes, you're right, Mo," his dad said. "If only more people in this world thought the way you do. I'm proud of you."

Then he turned to the police officer. "No, we won't be pressing charges. Instead, we'll try to help the thief. Can we go and meet him?"

5
FIRST GOAL

December 2010, Cairo Military Academy Stadium, Cairo, Egypt
SC Al Ahly v Al Mokawloon

"It's going to be today," Mohamed Elneny said, patting Mo on the back. "Trust me. You're going to get it today."

"I don't know," Mo frowned. "It just doesn't feel right."

"Well, enjoy it anyway," Elneny continued. "When we make our big moves to Europe, we won't play on Christmas Day any more. So you'll be the first Ballon d'Or winner to have scored on December 25th."

Mo smiled, but it didn't really lighten his mood. It had been seven months since he'd made his debut for the Al Mokawloon senior team, and he still hadn't scored his first goal. In that time, he'd had enough chances to score, but somehow it just hadn't happened.

And it was worrying him.

"Don't put so much pressure on yourself," Nasr had insisted. "You're one of the youngest players in the team – just relax and play your game. Goals will come. Worrying about it won't help."

Mo knew that his brother was right. The more he tried to shoot, to get into the box, to make space for himself in front of the keeper, the harder it seemed to be – and the rest of his game was slipping as well.

The new Al Mokawloon manager, Ivica Todorov, had also tried to put Mo at ease.

"It's not all about getting goals, Mo," he'd told him in one training session.

"But I'm a winger now. That's my job."

"No, no, no," Ivica had replied, shaking his head. "The striker gets goals – that's his one job. *You* have a lot of things to do out there. You have to dribble past

31

players, create chances, track back to help defend – and *then* you have to score some goals. You're doing all those other things really well. You keep doing that and the goals will follow."

Mo had nodded, feeling the tears welling up in his eyes. Scoring was what mattered most to him, because he knew that that was how he was going to prove himself to the football world.

"Hey, these tears are a good thing," Ivica had said, grabbing Mo's hand. "It shows that you care, it shows you're passionate – that this means something to you. Good things happen to people that love what they do."

Then Ivica had turned to the rest of the team. "This kid is 18," he'd told them, "and he's got more passion in him than the rest of you put together. I want all of you in tears after a match, showing some passion. Show me that you care."

Today, Mo had his biggest opportunity of the season. Al Mokawloon were struggling near the bottom of the league, and they badly needed points. Today, they were away at giants Al Ahly. If there was ever a game for Mo to turn up and get his first goal, this was it.

After a tough first half, Al Mokawloon were still in the game, with the score level at 0-0. Now, they could push on – go for a winner.

Early in the second half, Mohamed Adel picked up the ball in the middle of the pitch. He spotted Mo's run, moving towards goal. The ball was perfect, floating over the top of the defence. It would have been too long for some, but Mo was quick and he got there early.

He controlled it with one touch and set himself up to shoot, feeling the defenders breathing down his neck. He didn't catch it perfectly and it flew straight at the keeper. Then, somehow, it squirmed under the keeper and landed in the back of the net.

Mo had his first goal. It hadn't been his cleanest effort, or his best shot. He'd had so many better touches of the ball in his life, but he didn't care. He got to his knees and prayed, thanking God for helping him finally score.

Al Ahly scored a late equaliser to level the match, but, by that stage, Mo almost didn't care. He'd got his first goal for the club. Now, he knew for sure, more goals would follow.

6

SECOND FIRST GOAL

October 2011, Cairo International Stadium, Cairo, Egypt
World Cup Qualifier, Egypt v Niger

"Guys! Come on over," Hany Ramzy called out to his team during a training session at the Cairo International Stadium.

"Alright, guys, everyone welcome our latest recruit, the bright young star of Egyptian football … " Hany paused, extending an arm out towards Mo. "Mohamed Salah."

Mo nodded to the rest of the squad, avoiding eye contact. He didn't feel comfortable with the "bright young star of Egyptian football" bit, but since bursting onto the scene at Al Mokawloon over a year ago, he'd become the centre of attention in Egypt.

At just 19, he was already a regular in the first team and his exciting, attacking style of play had attracted a lot of interest.

That had included the attention of Egyptian national team manager, Hany Ramzy, who'd called Mo up.

Mo had made his national team debut a month ago, but not all of the regulars had been present that day, so Ramzy was now making sure that everyone knew each other before they went out for their first training session.

Mo glanced up nervously, catching the eye of his club team-mate, Mohamed Elneny, who flashed him a smile.

But Mo completely avoided looking at the player on Elneny's right, Egypt's legendary captain, Ahmed Hassan. Mo remembered watching Hassan when he was younger, not just at club level for Anderlecht and

Beşiktaş, but guiding Egypt to four African Cup of Nations titles.

And now they were both in the same room.

Minutes later, they were out on the training ground – and Mo realised that Hassan was approaching him. He'd been trying to work up the courage to speak to Hassan, to get some shooting advice, but Mo's heart-rate quickened as he realised he'd have to find that nerve now.

"So you're the new kid, then?" Hassan asked, looking Mo up and down.

"Yeah," Mo replied, barely getting the word out.

"I've seen some of your games," Hassan continued. "That was a nice goal against Al Ahly, and the one against Petrojet."

"Thanks," Mo smiled shyly.

"I assume you're thinking about going to Europe, making the move over. Let me offer you some free advice," Hassan offered.

"Oh, sure," Mo said, still a little starstruck.

"Go to a small league first. Even if the Prem or Spain or Italy come in for you, go for one of the smaller ones.

It's really different over there and you'll want time to adjust at your own pace. Trust me."

Mo nodded. He'd heard the same thing from other players, although at the moment it all seemed so premature. He'd barely got into the Al Mokawloon first team – he was hardly in a position to start turning down offers from Europe.

"Do you have any tips about football?" Mo asked. "Finishing, stuff like that?"

Hassan laughed. "Trust me, kid. I've watched you play," he said. "There's nothing I can teach you."

The next game for Egypt was a crucial World Cup qualifier against Niger in Cairo. It had been a long time since Egypt had qualified for a World Cup, and they needed to win this game to keep up the pressure.

Mo had already made his debut for Egypt in a 2-1 defeat against Sierra Leone the previous month but, now he was truly part of the squad, he was determined to be on the winning side with his country.

Today, he was starting up-front alongside Marwan Mohsen, and Mo could already sense that this was going to be his game.

His close friend and club team-mate, Mohamed Elneny, was in midfield behind him. Mo felt as if this had all been set up for him to get a goal today. If he did, it would be the first one for his country.

After a drab first half, Mohsen opened the scoring early on in the second, putting Egypt 1-0 up.

Then came Mo's turn.

He picked up the ball on the right wing and, spotting Elneny in the centre, played a pass inside, before bursting in behind the defence. Elneny timed his pass back to Mo perfectly, threading it through a gap in Niger's defence so that Mo stayed onside.

The keeper rushed off his line towards Mo, and there wasn't time to take more than one touch, so he whipped the ball towards the bottom-left corner.

GOAL!

There it was. His first goal for his country.

"That'll be the first of many," Hassan told him, as he celebrated. "Get used to that feeling."

Mo embraced his team-mates as they celebrated the goal, looking around the vast Cairo International Stadium.

He was now a fully-fledged international, famous across the whole of Egypt.

Now, he wanted the rest of the world.

7

SEALING A MOVE

March 2012, Stadion Rankhof, Basel, Switzerland
FC Basel v Egypt U23

"When do you think the season's coming back?"
Mohamed Elneny asked, turning towards Mo.

Mo shrugged.

Following political unrest and protests across Egypt, a
riot had broken out at the Port Said Stadium, in a match
between Al Ahly and Al Masry. To avoid anything like
it happening again, the government had moved quickly

to suspend the league, immediately bringing the season to a halt.

It had been a crushing blow for Mo and Elneny, who had both established themselves as Al Mokawloon and Egypt national team regulars. After struggling to score his first goal for the side, Mo had gone on to become a regular source of goals, and was attracting attention from clubs in Europe and beyond.

But, for the time being, the focus was on their national team. Both Mo and Elneny were part of Egypt's squad that was going to the Olympics. With no other football being played, the Egypt U23 team had arranged a number of friendlies to keep the players fit and fresh.

"Well?" Elneny asked again. "What do you think?"

Mo realised he hadn't answered Elneny's question.

"I've got no idea," he admitted.

"What are you thinking about?" Elneny asked. He'd spent enough time with Mo to recognise when something was on his mind.

"Do you remember the guy we met – from Basel?" he said.

"George?" Elneny replied. "The sporting director? The one who set up today's game, to help keep us fit for the Olympics, right?"

"Yeah … " Mo paused. "But he spoke to me separately – him and the owner. Basically, if I play well today, they're going to try and sign me. Sign a contract starting in July."

"No way!" Elneny gasped. "That's sick, Mo! I can't believe it! You're going all the way to Europe!"

"Maybe, maybe," Mo said, raising his hands, trying to calm his friend's excitement. "It's not set in stone. I have to play well today – and I'm starting on the bench, remember."

"You'll get on, though," Elneny replied. "It's just a formality, I bet. They're definitely going to sign you anyway, whatever happens."

"I hope so," Mo sighed. He hadn't really expected to be leaving Al Mokawloon so soon – he'd wanted to have a little more time to get into the first team, perhaps hit 20 goals in the Egyptian league.

But circumstances had forced his hand.

The game was level at half-time when Mo was given

the opportunity to come on. It was freezing cold in Basel, especially compared to the high heat that he was used to in Egypt, but he could feel the eyes of the crowd on him.

Mo didn't know whether the Basel fans were aware of the rumours linking him with their club. He couldn't see FC Basel's owner, or the Sporting Director, George Heitz, in the crowd, but he knew that they would be watching him.

He had 45 minutes to impress – 45 minutes to seal a move to Switzerland.

It only took 10 minutes for Mo to get his first goal – Egypt's second in the game. A ball was played across the face of goal from the left-hand side, and Mo was waiting on the far side. He burst in from behind the left-back, simply poking the ball past the keeper.

GOAL!

"Come on!" he roared, before regaining his composure and remembering that this was only a friendly. He tried not to show too much enthusiasm, but he knew that the goal would surely impress the Basel staff watching him.

Egypt added a third goal and then, with five minutes

left, Mo got his second. A bouncing ball over the top was miscontrolled by the defenders, and it fell in front of him. It was still bouncing when he blasted it into the top corner.

This time, he was calm enough not to celebrate too much. After all, he didn't need to go wild in front of the fans – there were only a couple of people he needed to impress, and his skills had already done the talking.

As the full-time whistle blew, Elneny came over to Mo, grabbing him by the shoulder. "Looks like I'll be waving goodbye to you at the airport!" Elneny laughed, putting his arm around Mo.

Mo was about to reply when he spotted two men approaching them. It was Basel's Sporting Director, George Heitz, and the club's chairman, Bernhard Heusler.

"That's them now, isn't it? I'll let you arrange your new contract," Elneny teased, walking away.

"Mo! George said you were good!" Bernhard exclaimed enthusiastically. "But he undersold you. You've got to be one of the quickest players I've ever seen. You were lightning out there!"

"Thank you," Mo said quietly, feeling a little shy.

"Look, Mo," George interjected. "I'll be blunt. We want to sign you. It's all been agreed with Al Mokawloon – we just need you to agree to it. A contract starting in June. You come over here, and you can be our replacement for Xherdan Shaqiri."

"What do you think?" Bernhard asked eagerly.

Mo paused for a few seconds. It was freezing cold here. He'd be away from the sun, away from his family, away from all his friends. It would be a new language, a new culture – everything would be different.

It would be a real challenge.

"Yes," he replied. "Yes. I want to do it."

8

THE NAME IS SALAH

April 2013, St Jakob-Park, Basel, Switzerland
Europa League Quarter-finals, FC Basel v Tottenham Hotspur

"Who'd have thought we'd end up here together?" Mohamed Elneny said, glancing up at the sky, where the rain had just started coming down thick and fast.

Mo shivered and zipped up his training top, pulling it tight. He'd only been at Basel for a couple of months when he'd been joined at the club by his friend and international team-mate, Mohamed Elneny.

"I thought I'd got rid of you, coming here!" Mo teased.

"I didn't have much choice, Mo – there's no football in Egypt!" Elneny replied.

Both players were very relieved to be at Basel together. Without Elneny, Mo wasn't sure he'd ever have got used to life here. A number of different languages were spoken within the Basel squad, but pretty much nobody spoke Arabic. The coaches and staff all encouraged Mo to learn English, but it was still difficult to communicate with his team-mates on and off the pitch.

It wasn't just the language issue that was tricky. Mo had been signed as a replacement for Xherdan Shaqiri, who had departed for Bayern Munich. Shaqiri had come through the Basel academy – and he'd been hugely popular with the fans. Now he'd been replaced by an unknown 20-year-old from the Egyptian league. Mo would need to make sure he won the fans over.

There were many times when he'd found the pressure difficult to deal with, although he knew that, if he was to succeed as a professional player, he had to move beyond Egypt at some point.

It also helped that Mo had scored in just his second league game for Basel, in a comfortable 2-0 win over Lausanne.

The style of football in Switzerland was slightly different to back in Egypt, and Basel often used Mo's pace to break out if they were under pressure. Very quickly, Mo endeared himself to the Basel fans and the rest of his team.

Unlike Al Mokawloon in Egypt, Basel were the dominant team in Switzerland and they quickly moved a long way clear at the top of the Swiss Super League.

But the real focus for Mo was the European matches. These were the games against teams that he'd seen on TV as a kid, the teams that the big players had played for.

Basel had been knocked out of Champions League qualifying and had ended up in the Europa League, and Mo had played regularly in these games. But so far they hadn't played any of the big guns, any of the teams that Mo had dreamt about playing against.

But tonight, that was going to change. Tonight, Basel were up against Tottenham Hotspur.

Mo had watched plenty of Premier League games on TV as a kid – and even more since he'd joined Basel – so he knew tonight's opponents well.

Spurs were an established Premier League team, with great players, including Gareth Bale, Jan Vertonghen and Hugo Lloris, and a huge fanbase. So this was a real opportunity for Mo to impress against a Premier League side and to begin building a reputation for himself in Europe.

Basel had done well to earn a 2-2 draw away from home in the first leg, and now they had a good chance of getting themselves into the semi-finals. But nobody underestimated how tough it was going to be.

"They're putting Basel's game on the main channel here," Nasr had told Mo on the phone. "It's crazy to think that everyone in Egypt will be watching a match between an English and a Swiss team, just because of you!"

"I'll do my best to put on a show," Mo had replied cheekily.

The rain was coming down hard as the match kicked off.

The game got off to the worst possible start for Basel, when Clint Dempsey rounded their keeper and put Spurs into the lead. All of Basel's hard work in the first leg had been cancelled out after just 23 minutes.

With Spurs one goal up and now in the ascendancy, Basel had to be careful not to go two down and lose the game entirely.

But a few minutes later, Elneny nipped in, winning the ball off Mousa Dembélé in the Spurs midfield. Mo was already running, sprinting away down the right-hand side, his hand up, signalling for the ball. The ball came to Marco Streller, who quickly played it on to Mo.

Mo's first touch was heavy, and the ball rolled several yards in front of him. He saw Jan Vertonghen closing in, going for the tackle, and realised that there was no time for a second touch. With his left foot, he poked the ball towards the near post. The ball skidded past keeper Brad Friedel and landed in the back of the net.

GOAL!

Mo turned towards his team-mates in celebration, waving his arms in the air. It was Mo's first goal in

Europe, and it had come against one of the biggest teams in England.

He may have been an unknown when he'd joined Basel, but now everyone was starting to know the name "Salah".

9

ON THE RADAR

November 2013, St Jakob-Park, Basel, Switzerland
UEFA Champions League Group Stage, FC Basel v Chelsea

"Who are you gonna sign for, then?" Elneny asked Mo.
"Liverpool? Inter Milan? Maybe even Barcelona or Real
Madrid?"

"They're not going for me," Mo scoffed. "Nobody is.
At least, I've not heard anything from anyone."

Mo's first season in Europe had ended with his first
professional trophy, as Basel had won the league for yet

another season. With five goals and four assists, Mo was even named Swiss Super League Player of the Year, in his first season in Switzerland.

He had followed up his goal against Spurs with another against Chelsea in the semi-finals, although Basel had been knocked out on aggregate. But it had been enough to draw the attention of a number of teams in Europe.

Despite his successes, there were still those who weren't impressed. Murat Yakin, the Basel manager, was particularly insistent that there was more that Mo could add to his game.

Basel had been drawn against Chelsea in their Champions League group for the new season and, with the second game against Chelsea coming up, Yakin sat Mo down.

"You want to play at the top level, yeah Mo?" he asked. "You want to go to Italy? England? Spain?"

Mo hesitated, not sure what to say.

"It's OK," Yakin added. "Nobody wants to stay in Switzerland forever. We know that."

Yakin paused, appearing to change the subject.

"What do you think when you get through on goal? What's going through your mind? Are you planning where to shoot? Are you thinking about the keeper?"

Mo shrugged. "I guess. Yeah – I'm just thinking about hitting it hard."

"That's OK," Yakin nodded. "That's what I used to do too. I was never much of a finisher so, yeah – hit it hard, hope for the best."

He paused, smiling a little.

"But I was a centre-back, Mo," he added. "I didn't want to be a finisher. I didn't *need* to be. Where do you want to play? Left wing? Right wing?"

Mo nodded.

"A few years ago, being quick and getting in behind was enough for a winger," Yakin continued. "It was the striker that scored the goals. And, believe me, you're quick enough and talented enough – you could be a top-class striker, Mo."

Yakin paused, making sure that Mo was listening.

"My brother was a top-class striker. I spoke to him about this – about what he'd be thinking on the pitch. He would already have picked his spot *before* the ball had even come to him. He didn't need to think about where he was going to put it. He already knew."

Mo nodded. "You want me to do that?"

"I want you to think about it," Murat replied. "You're still young. But I want you to try to add this to your game. Because you could be hitting 20, 25 goals a season. You've got a brilliant left foot and you're one of the quickest players in Europe right now."

Mo knew the gaffer was right. His finishing had always been a weak part of his game. For every goal that he'd score, there would be another three or four chances that would go wide.

Mo's next opportunity to impress came in the game against Chelsea. Basel had already beaten them once this season in the Champions League, and a second win would really make a statement.

Added to that, Mo had scored in his last two games, and he was desperate to make it three in three.

Mo was playing on the right-hand side, taking on Chelsea's left-hand side pairing of Willian and César Azpilicueta. He was involved in a battle with them pretty much from the get go, fighting to win the ball back, dribbling at them, trying to knock the ball past them.

Then, after 20 minutes or so, the chances started to come. First, a long range effort was palmed over by Petr Čech, then another shot bounced off the floor and was pushed wide.

"Come on, Mo!" Granit Xhaka called to him. "I thought you wanted a goal."

The chances continued to come, with Mo putting on the best display of his career. But he still couldn't get that goal.

"Mo! Switch to the left wing!" manager Murat Yakin shouted over to him. With the game trickling out, Mo moved over to the left-hand side. One last opportunity was all he needed.

A long ball over the top from Basel centre-back Fabian Schär was exactly what Mo needed. He darted in behind the slower Chelsea right-back, Branislav Ivanović, knocking the ball ahead of him to use his speed.

As he dribbled into the box, Mo already knew what he was going to do. With a swing of his left foot, he fired the ball past Čech.

GOAL!

He'd scored against Chelsea once again.

And even more than that, he'd won the game for Basel and sent them into the next round of the Champions League.

At full-time, Mo noticed Chelsea's manager, José Mourinho, walking over to him.

"That was some display out there," Mourinho said, patting him on the back. "You keep scoring against us, don't you?"

Mo shrugged and grinned, feeling embarrassed. "Sorry."

"Well, we'll have to rectify that," Mourinho replied. "You'll have to come and join us one day."

Mourinho turned and walked away without giving Mo time to reply.

Mo simply stood there, in a state of shock. He'd just put himself on the radar of one of the best managers – and one of the biggest clubs – in Europe.

10
KEEP TAKING THE CHANCES

March 2014, Stamford Bridge, Chelsea, London
Chelsea v Arsenal

"Come to Liverpool," Brendan Rodgers had begged down the phone. "We're building something special here. Suárez, Sturridge and Coutinho were all at your level when they joined us – and now they've exploded! Come to Liverpool and become a legend, Mo. Win us our first title in 30 years!"

It had been a passionate speech and, for a long

time, Mo had dwelt on the prospect. He'd heard about Anfield, Liverpool's famous stadium, he'd heard about their fans, about their legendary players like Steven Gerrard and Fernando Torres.

But there was another offer on the table too. When Mourinho had told Mo that he needed him to join Chelsea, it hadn't just been empty words. The club had followed up with an offer during the January transfer window, matching Liverpool's bid and meeting Basel's asking price of 11 million pounds.

Eleven million! Even now, Mo couldn't believe that price. It was a huge fee for a player of his age, who'd only been in Switzerland for a couple of seasons.

There were so few Egyptian players playing at the top level in the Premier League – or in the other big leagues across Europe. Wherever he went, this move would make him the biggest star in his country.

What should he do? Mo turned to the players at Basel for advice. Most were sad to see him go, but none were surprised. His performances over the last year had been electric, and it was only a matter of time before he'd be snapped up.

"Liverpool are giants. The fans are incredible," one player would say.

"Chelsea won the Champions League only two years ago. José's taken them to another level," another said.

"José's a born winner," another added. "But he's got Hazard, Schürrle, Willian, Oscar ... Are you replacing them?"

"Liverpool haven't won anything in years!"

Then, when Mo spoke to his brother back home, Nasr echoed what most of the players had been telling him.

"Liverpool are doing well," Nasr mused, "but they haven't won anything for years. Chelsea are the big guns. José's won so many trophies – he's a legend. If you go there, you'll win something, Mo, for sure. You'll just have to be patient, though. You might not gets starts straight away."

That was enough to convince Mo. He'd been sceptical about Liverpool from the beginning. They were top of the league at the moment, but he could hardly be certain that that was going to last.

Chelsea were always near the top – and he still

remembered the conversation with José after Basel had played Chelsea. Mourinho already knew what Mo could do.

His mind was made up. It would be Chelsea.

"I don't know how to thank you for giving me the opportunity to play in Europe," Mo said to George Heitz, on his last day at Basel.

"We should be the ones thanking you, Mo! Because of you, many young African talents will want to come to Basel. We knew we'd always be a stepping stone for you – and you've done us proud."

As soon as Mo arrived in London, he was grateful that he'd learned English whilst he'd been at Basel. It meant that language was one less thing to worry about.

Training with Basel had been a big step up from Al Mokawloon, but working with Chelsea was a world away from anything he'd experienced before.

Mo had to pinch himself when he saw his new team-mates at the Cobham Training Centre. A glance to his left and he saw Eden Hazard dribbling at Ashley Cole and John Terry. To his right, Frank Lampard was pinging passes to Samuel Eto'o and Fernando Torres.

Not to mention the likes of Petr Čech, Willian, Oscar and Branislav Ivanović. Every player was a superstar.

And overseeing it all was the ringmaster, José Mourinho, the man who had won titles in four different countries, who'd won the Champions League twice. He was one of the greatest managers of all time.

And now Mo was rubbing shoulders with all of them.

Nasr had been right in saying that his time at Chelsea might start slowly. Mo played just 13 minutes in his first eight games, and he was often an unused substitute, spending the whole game on the bench.

But José had warned him as much. "You're going to be thrown into the deep end here," he told him. "And you'll have to take your chances when they come, Mo. We're in a title race – and we're fighting for the FA Cup and Champions League as well. I can't go giving you minutes to get you up to speed."

Mo nodded.

"But when the opportunity comes, you must be ruthless. Show me why I signed you, show me why you should play in front of Hazard and Willian. Show me that, and I will play you."

Chelsea's next game was a huge clash against Arsenal and, once more, Mo found himself starting on the bench, next to Senegalese striker Demba Ba and Fernando Torres.

"I think he'll give you some minutes today, Mo," Demba said, leaning over. "Arsenal play quite open – your pace will be devastating."

"I don't know," Mo shrugged, feeling resigned. "I'm not sure there's anything I can do to get in the team now."

"He does this to everyone," Demba insisted. "He's easing you in, working out what kind of guy you are. You've been like Messi in training, everyone knows it. He's going to start giving you more minutes."

Mo wasn't so sure, but as Chelsea raced into a 4-0 lead and Arsenal went down to 10 men, he began to feel more optimistic.

Chelsea had control of the game, and there were fewer risks now.

When Oscar added a fifth, midway through the second half, Mo got the call.

"Mo! Get over here, you're coming on!" José called.

Mo stripped off his tracksuit as quickly as possible and ran over to Mourinho on the touchline.

"Pressure's off today. Get used to playing at the Bridge, play your game, and if you find yourself in front of goal, show me what you're made of," José told him.

Mo quickly realised that Demba Ba had been right about Arsenal being open. With only 10 men, they were struggling to keep track of the movement of Chelsea's attackers.

Nemanja Matić picked the ball up in midfield and Mo was already moving, watching the Arsenal offside line and drifting over to the left-hand side, lurking just on the shoulder of the defence.

Matić had spotted him and drifted a ball over the top. The Arsenal defence were sure that Mo was offside and they stepped up, leaving him an acre of space in behind. But they had got it wrong and he had timed his run to perfection. He was onside.

Mo flew in behind, taking the ball with him and bearing down on goal. The Arsenal keeper came out, but Mo had all the time in the world to pick his spot and slide it past him into the net.

It was his first Chelsea goal and he pointed back at Matic, thanking him for the pass, before getting to his knees and kissing the ground in prayer, the way he celebrated all his goals.

"That's got to impress him," he muttered to himself, glancing over at José, who was still celebrating the goal.

"Looks like your Chelsea career is about to take off!" Demba said at the final whistle, as he ran onto the pitch and put his arm around Mo.

"I just have to keep taking the chances I'm given," Mo grinned. "Just like the boss said."

II

ITALIAN DETOUR

March 2015, Allianz Stadium, Turin, Italy
Coppa Italia Semi-Final First Leg, Juventus v Fiorentina

"I wouldn't say it's been a failure … " Nasr hesitated, as he saw the look on Mo's face.

"José would," Mo said. "Most of Egypt would. The Chelsea fans would too."

Mo had thought that the goal against Arsenal would kick-start his Chelsea career, but it hadn't happened – and, to make matters worse, Chelsea had finished the season without a trophy. Then Diego Costa and Cesc Fàbregas had arrived over the summer, but Mo remained mostly on the bench.

Then, after a struggling performance in the League Cup against Shrewsbury, Mo was publicly called out by José. And privately, the words weren't much kinder.

"How about a loan?" José had said to him one morning after training. "You've improved so much, but we're in a title race again here. I can't guarantee you minutes. A loan would be good for you."

"I can fight for my place," Mo had replied, but a look from José said everything. It was a loan – or sit matches out for the rest of the season.

"I suggest Fiorentina," José continued. "I know the league well – you'll do really well out there. We don't want to lose you, Mo. We want you to get some more games under your belt, come back and continue where you left off. Trust me, there's a big role for you here … "

Mo was no longer listening. He knew that José was only suggesting a temporary move, a loan, but he didn't believe it. And he could sense that José didn't either.

It didn't take long for Mo to realise why José had

suggested Fiorentina. Chelsea were in talks to sign Juan Cuadrado, another winger, from the club, and Mo was being sent the other way as part of the deal.

Mo knew that, having only just signed him, Chelsea couldn't sell him yet. But in a few years, no doubt, they would probably sell him on.

The move happened in the January transfer window and, as it happened, Mo quickly realised that he preferred Fiorentina to Chelsea. The weather was more pleasant, there was less intensity in the training and in the games, and everyone seemed to get along with each other – far better than at Chelsea.

José Mourinho's looming presence had no equivalent here, and most of the players seemed happier and better off for it. Fiorentina were also doing well in the league, pushing to finish in the top-four and qualify for the Champions League. They were also doing well in both the Europa League and the Cup.

Slotting into the right-wing position that Cuadrado had just vacated, Mo settled quickly, forming a good partnership with Mario Gómez and scoring in three of his first four games.

Fiorentina's next game was the Coppa Italia semi-final first leg, away at Juventus, the biggest team in Italy. It had been 14 years since Fiorentina had last won the trophy, and reaching the final would easily be the biggest moment in the club's recent history.

Juventus had rested players for the game, with an eye on securing the league title and going deep into the Champions League, but, even so, they were still a formidable team.

"You're in the form of your life, Mo," Fiorentina's manager, Vicenzo Montella, told him in the dressing room before kick-off. "Believe in yourself – even a team like Juventus can't defend against you."

It took just 11 minutes for the deadlock to be broken. From the start, Juve piled on the pressure, but then the ball was nodded clear by Fiorentina, to where Mo was waiting. There was nobody else in purple with him and he was still in his own half, surrounded by Juventus players. He controlled the ball with his left foot and began sprinting forwards, taking the ball with him. The defenders pursued him, but they weren't catching him now.

He flicked the ball around another defender and

chased after it, shrugging off an attempted challenge. He was still a long way from goal, and defenders were still behind him, tugging at his shirt and nipping at his heels. But they couldn't stop him now.

As he entered the box, he fired a shot, blasting the ball hard into the top corner, past the desperate dive of the keeper.

GOAL!

The home fans were stunned into silence as the small section of Fiorentina fans celebrated, and Mo was quickly mobbed by his team-mates.

"That's one of the best goals I've ever seen," Milan Badelj told him.

Juventus came back strongly and, just 10 minutes later, Fernando Llorente powered home a header to equalise. The crowd were up now, getting behind the men in black and white. Fiorentina had to hold firm.

Mo was a frustrated passenger for most of it, looking on as his team defended resolutely. He would try to support Mario Gómez when the ball came forward, but he was very quickly swarmed by defenders, clearly unwilling to give him the space to score another.

Then, early in the second half, Mo found his space and got his chance. Juventus attempted to play out from the back, but Joaquín nipped in first, blocking the ball on the edge of the Juventus area.

It came to Mo, who raced into the box, holding off the challenge from a defender. He opened himself up and slotted the ball past the keeper and into the back of the net. Once more, Fiorentina had the lead.

Juventus pushed forward again, throwing on strikers Carlos Tevez and Álvaro Morata to try to equalise, but Fiorentina managed to hold on until the final whistle.

Thanks to Mo's two goals, Fiorentina had taken a shock win at the home of Italy's best team.

It felt just like when Mo had scored the winning goals for Basel, against Chelsea. Then, he'd been on top of the world – and had got himself on the radar of the big clubs.

But he knew that this was different. They'd all told him that he'd only get one chance at a big club like Chelsea – but now Mo knew he was going to change all of that.

He was going to prove them all wrong.

12
ITALIAN IDOL

August 2015, Trigoria Training Ground, Roma, Italy

"I've got a club for you, Mo," his agent told him. "The offer's come out of nowhere. Somewhere new, but not too far from where you are now. They're a big one, possibly title-challengers ... "

"Who is it?" Mo interrupted. That was all he really wanted to know.

"Roma," his agent replied.

"Roma?" Mo echoed.

"They want you on loan at first, but they're looking at making it permanent at the end of the year. Eighteen million euros or so. Chelsea are happy with it, I think."

His agent was right – it wouldn't be a move far away, and Mo was glad about that. He'd enjoyed his time in Serie A so far, and he thought life in Rome might suit him.

"They've got some great players," his agent continued, "and I've heard they want to bring in Edin Džeko to help give Totti one last chance at winning the title."

"Totti!" Mo burst out. Although Francesco was almost 40 now, and not the player he once was, he was still Roma's golden boy – and the player Mo had idolised back in Egypt. There was no chance Mo was going to turn down the opportunity to play alongside him.

Even though he'd only been at Fiorentina since January, Mo had finished the season as their third top goalscorer, with nine goals. But his brace against Juventus hadn't been enough to send Fiorentina into the Coppa Italia final, as the Italian champions had roared back to win the second leg 3-0.

Fiorentina had also been knocked out at the semi-final stage of the Europa League by eventual winners Sevilla, ending the reign of Vicenzo Montella.

Mo's loan move had been agreed for 18 months, but with the manager who'd signed him gone, his remaining 12 months in Florence were now in doubt.

Which was why Mo had asked his agent to see if there was any interest in him.

As it turned out, his agent had been right about Roma bringing in some new players to push for the title. Everything was quickly agreed, and Mo was joined at the club by Wojciech Szczęsny, Antonio Rüdiger, Edin Džeko and Lucas Digne, as Roma looked to establish a title-winning side.

It didn't take long for Mo to settle at Roma. He scored five goals in his first nine games, and even an injury and a change of manager didn't put him off his stride.

But the biggest thing for Mo, by far, was being around Francesco Totti. Mo had met some big names during his career so far, especially during his time at Chelsea, but Totti topped the lot.

Totti was worshipped in Rome like a god, and it was a level of admiration that Mo hadn't seen before. Yet Mo could see that it might be something *he'd* have to get used to in time.

Back home in Egypt, Mo was now the country's biggest star and he already had almost 50 caps and over 20 goals to his name. He was adored back there, almost to the same extent as Totti in Rome. But Mo hadn't won anything with his country. He couldn't bear to let them down.

"How do you cope with the pressure from the fans? What if we don't deliver?" he asked Francesco.

"You can't let yourself get caught up in it," Francesco replied. "The fans don't expect you to win every game, but they want you to leave everything out there on the pitch. If you lose, but you've given everything, they will still love you."

"I hope that's true," Mo replied. "I'm not sure that winning a trophy with Egypt is going to be possible."

"If you do what I'm telling you," Francesco smiled as he put an arm on Mo's shoulder, "it won't matter."

13
MAGICAL

November 2016, Stadio Olimpico, Rome, Italy
AS Roma v Bologna

"Goals, goals, goals. That's how we're going to win the title." There was an intensity to Roma manager Luciano Spalletti as he spoke.

He wasn't just saying this to fire the players up – Mo could see that he really believed what he was telling them. Spalletti was convinced that this was the best way for Roma to wrestle the title away from Juventus.

Spalletti had taken over midway through last season and had immediately transformed Roma, leading them on a 16-game unbeaten run.

"We've got Mo, Edin, Perotti, Stéphane ... " he continued. "We have the best attacking players in this league – and they haven't even realised it."

Mo looked across the room at Francesco Totti, sitting opposite him. Totti had seen it all at Roma. He'd lifted titles *and* experienced some of their lowest ebbs. He would be able to see through anyone over-promising, announcing things they couldn't deliver.

Looking at Totti's face, all Mo could see was belief. Totti believed – and now, so did Mo.

Spalletti was more than just words, though. He worked closely with the players in training sessions to make sure that the team could deliver. With Mo, Spalletti focused on his interplay with Edin Džeko.

"Edin controls it – he has his back to goal," Spalletti barked, throwing the ball at Džeko's chest.

"Mo, where are you?" he roared. "You need to get around him, behind him, in front of him. Don't stop moving."

"Lose your marker!" Spalletti ordered, as Džeko held onto the ball and grappled with his own defender.

"Now find him, Edin!"

The ball came Mo's way and he controlled it. Head down, he burst into the box, far on the right-hand side.

"Now get it back to him, Mo!" Spalletti bellowed again.

Without looking up, Mo fired the ball back to where he thought Edin was. The ball hurtled into the box, but was behind the striker, who stretched out a leg but couldn't reach it.

"Mo!" Spalletti shouted, calling him over. "Where are your eyes? Are they on top of your head?"

Mo shook his head, confused.

"Then why are you looking down? You know you have the ball – you don't need to check it's still there. Watch the players, the movement. You scored a lot of goals last year, but you can get double the assists."

Spalletti was right about Roma's attacking potential. They scored 26 goals in their first 11 games, with Mo getting five goals and five assists. Now they were in second place, on the heels of Juventus.

A win against today's opponents, Bologna, would keep them well in the hunt.

The nerves of the home fans were calmed inside 15 minutes, when Diego Perotti wriggled his way into the box and pulled the ball back to where Mo was waiting. Mo's shot was on target, but was blocked by the outstretched leg of a Bologna defender.

The leg wasn't enough, and the ball trickled under the defender, past the keeper and over the line.

"Surely you're not claiming that?" Edin Džeko scoffed.

"That was going in!" Mo protested. "I'm having that."

Roma continued to press hard, with Perotti, Nainggolan and Džeko all getting chances – with Mo setting all of them up.

As the second half began, there were fewer laughs and more nervous glances, as the chances continued to go wide. They needed that second goal.

Then Mo found himself played through with an exquisite pass from Kevin Strootman. Mo took it in his stride, racing in on the keeper. He left it late, but eventually opened his body up and slid the ball past the keeper. He'd got Roma's second.

Mo could feel the tension lift amongst the players and the fans inside the Stadio Olimpico. With a two-goal lead, they felt that they could relax now.

But Mo couldn't. He was always pushing – and he was very aware that he hadn't yet scored a hat-trick in his career. With the way Roma were creating chances, could he get another goal today?

Just 10 minutes after his second goal, a shot from Edin Džeko was palmed away by the keeper – and Mo raced in to tap it over the line. He had his hat-trick – and at the home of his idol, Francesco Totti, too.

A few moments later, Mo was substituted, to rapturous applause and a standing ovation. He could hear his name being chanted from all corners of the stadium.

He had once asked Totti what it was like to be adored like this and, although this was only a fraction of what Totti experienced, it was magical.

He could get used to this.

14
WELCOME TO OUR FAMILY

August 2017, Anfield, Liverpool, England
Liverpool v Arsenal

"What's up?" Mo asked his agent, answering the phone call.

"Are you sitting down?"

"You sound in a good mood," Mo replied.

With all the uncertainty at Roma, Mo wasn't feeling very positive about his future at the club. Roma had been on fire in Serie A, blasting aside all those who tried to get near them – all except one. Juventus had been a level above them all season and had finished top, with Roma in a heartbreaking second place.

Then Luciano Spalletti had departed for Inter Milan, hand-picked as the man to lead them back into the top four. There were also whispered rumours that the club were going to fail financial fair play regulations. If so, there would have to be sales – and Mo would be top of the list.

So Mo couldn't quite understand why his agent was sounding so cheerful.

"Well, Mo," his agent replied. "I've got some news. You've had scouts keeping an eye on you over the last couple of seasons! And now we have an offer on the table – from the very team that wanted you four years ago."

"Liverpool … " Mo said under his breath.

"Yeah, Liverpool. They want you. A lot has changed there recently. Steven Gerrard has retired, Jürgen Klopp has replaced Brendan Rodgers, and they look destined for big things. It's a step up from Roma – and I think it's a no-brainer."

Mo knew that, after leaving Chelsea with just two

goals in 19 appearances, he had unfinished business in the Premier League. At the age of 25, he was now entering his prime as a player. Where else to play the best football of his career than in England?

"You're twice the player now, compared to when you left Chelsea," his agent told him. "Prove to everyone that Mourinho made a mistake in letting you go."

In the end, the transfer was simple. The fee was almost 40 million euros, making him the joint most expensive African player of all time, alongside his new team-mate Sadio Mané.

Mo was handed the number 11 shirt, the one he had enjoyed wearing at Roma, and within a week he was training with his new team-mates.

"We need to ease you in, so you can get used to how we play," Klopp told Mo, "but this happens to everyone who's new to my team. If you work hard, then good things will happen for you and the club."

Jürgen Klopp was the direct opposite to Mourinho. He was warm and always wore a smile, and there was no icing-out of players he disliked. He also encouraged fast, attacking play, which suited Mo well.

Mo scored in his first game, a 3-3 draw with Watford, but then only played 29 minutes off the bench in the next game, a 1-0 win over Crystal Palace at Anfield.

He knew that Klopp was easing him in, but nevertheless he was frustrated. He didn't want a repeat of the struggle to get game time that he'd had at Chelsea.

"You've got to trust the process with Jürgen," Liverpool's assistant manager, Pep Lijnders, told Mo. "Trust me, he knows what's best for you – and for the team – better than you know yourself. You'll play when the time is right."

With Philippe Coutinho injured, that time turned out to be Liverpool's next game, against Arsenal. Mo was thrown into the starting line-up, alongside Mané and Roberto Firmino.

Firmino opened the scoring inside 20 minutes, with a thumping header from a Joe Gomez cross. Mané added a goal just before half-time, cutting inside and curling into the far corner.

Liverpool were 2-0 up.

In the second half, it was Mo's turn. Twelve minutes

in, he burst through, racing into the Arsenal half. The defenders were behind him, chasing him down, but he knew they weren't going to catch him. Whatever league you were playing in, when you had a clear pitch in front of you, it was all the same.

The keeper came out, arms outstretched, but it wasn't enough. Mo tucked the ball past him and watched it roll into the back of the net.

GOAL!

He turned to the Liverpool fans, arms raised in celebration. He had heard stories of the noise at Anfield, how it was famous for the big European nights, how the Kop could "suck" the ball into the net. But he'd never really experienced it, even when he'd played there before.

The noise that came following his goal was on another level. It might be just an early-season goal, and it might not be a winner – Liverpool were now 3-0 up – but it was Mo's first goal for Liverpool at the stadium.

That's what they were celebrating. They were welcoming him into their family.

He was a Liverpool player now.

15
ANOTHER RECORD

May 2018, Anfield, Liverpool, England
Liverpool v Brighton & Hove Albion

"Looks like I was wrong about you, Mo," Jürgen Klopp laughed, after a particularly tough training session. "I thought you'd need to be eased in, given time to adapt to the Prem once again."

"Sorry, boss," Mo laughed, a big grin on his face.

Mo had followed up his goals against Arsenal and Watford with goals against Burnley, Leicester and

Spurs. Then a brace at West Ham, and another brace against Southampton – and then against Stoke. The goals had kept on flowing, and not just in the Premier League.

Mo had had a small taste of the Champions League during his time at Roma and Basel, but this was the first time he'd had an extended run in the competition, and he was loving it.

The records had begun to tumble too. He was the second-fastest player to reach 20 goals for Liverpool, doing so in just 26 games.

Mo had formed a prolific front-three with Sadio Mané and Roberto Firmino, and the team was adding its own records, becoming the first team to win four consecutive Premier League away games by more than three goals.

Mo had been part of a front four, but in January, Philippe Coutinho had departed for Barcelona, for an enormous fee of over 100 million euros.

"Why would he leave?" Mo asked his team-mates. "Can't he see what's happening here, what we're building?"

Perhaps it was his experiences at Chelsea that had scarred him, but Mo couldn't understand why you'd throw away a manager like Jürgen Klopp or a club like Liverpool.

"He wants to win the Champions League," Sadio Mané told him. "He thinks Barca can do that."

"It *is* Barcelona, to be fair," Firmino added. "Who wouldn't want to play there?"

"I was more of a Madrid man myself," Mo frowned.

Mo hadn't really considered moving on from Liverpool, or going for a move to one of his dream clubs like Real Madrid. It just hadn't seemed realistic.

But now there was no doubt that he had established himself as one of the best players in the world. Already this season, he'd overtaken both Harry Kane and Lionel Messi in the number of goals scored, to become the highest-scoring player in Europe.

Every time he cut inside on his left foot and whipped a shot towards goal, the crowd were up and celebrating before it had even left his foot. He was at the top of his game, he was winning matches, and the Kop were with him all the way. Life was good.

Liverpool had slipped behind City in the title race, but were well on course for confirming a Champions League finish – which had been their aim at the start of the season. They were also doing well in the competition itself.

A semi-final meeting with Mo's former club, Roma, ended with Liverpool triumphing 7-6 on aggregate, with Mo scoring twice and setting up two more. It put Liverpool into the final, where they would take on Real Madrid.

Then, to cap a brilliant few months, at the start of May, Mo was awarded the PFA Player of the Year Award, sealing his place as the best player in the country – and one of the best in the world.

The final Liverpool game of the Premier League season rolled around a few weeks later, against Brighton, although most players and fans at Liverpool had their eye on the prize of the Champions League final, which was being played after the end of the season.

Mo understood the desire to concentrate on the final, but he had his own reasons for focusing particularly on the Brighton game.

"The record's 31," his brother, Nasr, had told him. Week after week, Nasr had been repeating it – over the phone, in person, via message. "The record's 31."

It was the current record for the number of goals scored by a player in a single, 38-game Premier League season. The record was held jointly by Luis Suárez, Cristiano Ronaldo and Alan Shearer.

And now, with one game left in the season, Mo stood alongside them all, on 31 goals. If he scored in the final game against Brighton, his name would forever be in the Premier League record books for the most goals scored in a season.

On top of that, Liverpool also needed a win to secure their spot in the Champions League for next season.

Even if it hadn't been an important game, there was no chance Mo would have let Klopp rest him. He wanted that record.

Before the game, Mo made sure that everyone knew that he was going for the record.

"Sadio, make sure you get me the ball if you burst through – I'll only need it once."

"Trent, if you can get those passes into me … "

"Hendo, make sure you float those crosses my way."

Mo needed that goal – and he didn't care how he got it.

Fortunately, Mo didn't have to wait long. Just 26 minutes into the game, Liverpool found their opening, with Dominic Solanke flicking the ball into the box. It rebounded off a Brighton defender and came towards Mo.

With his back to goal, he spun, getting the ball onto his left foot, before drilling it into the bottom corner.

GOAL number 32!

He raced towards the corner, screaming, shouting and punching the air, as the Liverpool fans went mad with him. The tension had been released – he had his goal – and the record.

With that job done, Mo could now start to think about the momentous game next week – the Champions League final, against Real Madrid.

He could start to picture himself holding the Champions League trophy.

16
ON AND OFF THE WORLD STAGE

June 2018, Gazprom Arena, Saint Petersburg, Russia
FIFA World Cup, Russia v Egypt

"I can do this," Mo said to himself, under his breath.

He placed the ball down on the penalty spot, looked at the Russian keeper and slowly exhaled. He flexed his shoulder instinctively, feeling the pain shooting down the left-hand side of his body.

It had barely been a month since he'd finished the season, with his record-breaking 32nd Premier League goal, against Brighton – his 44th in all competitions. It had been the greatest moment of his career so far, and it had felt like the ultimate high.

There had still been the small matter of the Champions League final, against giants Real Madrid. The Spanish club had already won the trophy a staggering twelve times, and Liverpool had been talked about as the underdogs. But Liverpool fans had known that, with Mo in the team, they had every chance of going all the way.

For half an hour, the game had been even – both teams poking and probing, working each other out. Then, as Mo had grappled with Sergio Ramos, they'd both tumbled and fallen to the floor.

Mo's left arm had been caught on the wrong side of his body and, as they fell, it twisted and pulled painfully. There had been some accusations that Ramos had held onto Mo's arm in an attempt to injure him deliberately.

Either way, Mo hadn't cared. Deliberate or not, he'd known his game was done.

He'd allowed the tears to flow as he'd been stretchered off. The pain in his shoulder had actually helped, giving him something to focus on. Anything to avoid thinking about the fact he'd come off in the biggest game of his career.

For him, the Champions League final was over at that point, but Mo then started to worry about the World Cup that was coming up. Egypt were back in it for the first time in almost 30 years, and Mo was desperate to be a part of it.

But would he be fit in time?

As he was helped into the dressing room, he grabbed the physio with his good arm.

"The World Cup," he croaked, making eye contact. They both knew what was being asked.

"We can't think like that … " the physio began.

"Just tell me," Mo insisted. He had to know now.

"I don't know, Mo," the physio shrugged. "That's the truth. I don't know right now."

Mo was lying in the dressing room when the news came in that Real Madrid had beaten Liverpool 3-1, helped by a sensational overhead kick from Gareth Bale.

Mo didn't waste time thinking about what might

have happened if he'd stayed on the pitch. Instead, he turned his attention to the World Cup.

In a qualifier against Congo, Mo had scored a dramatic penalty in the last minute, to secure Egypt's place at the tournament. Both his team-mates and the Egyptian fans knew that, if it wasn't for Mo, they'd have no chance of making the tournament.

Mo had been offered a house in Egypt for scoring the goal, but he'd asked for a donation to be made to his home village of Nagrig instead.

Mo returned to Nagrig every Ramadan, presenting prizes to children in the village, playing table tennis and pool with his friends, signing autographs and posing with everyone who asked for a picture.

"I still can't believe that becoming one of the best footballers in the world hasn't changed you," Nasr told him, after Mo had signed a Liverpool shirt for a small boy.

"You remember when we were that tall, dreaming of playing at the World Cup?" Mo asked, pointing to the boy he'd just signed the Liverpool shirt for.

"Seems like a lifetime ago," Nasr replied, "but now you're going to make that dream come true."

"Am I, though?" Mo raised his injured shoulder.

"Think about how much you mean to Egyptians," Nasr said, his tone suddenly becoming more serious. "Even if you're injured, you have to at least travel with the squad. You're the face of this country."

Not long after that, Mo was included in Egypt's squad for the World Cup finals. Their manager, Héctor Cúper, was bullish.

"We need you, Mo," he said. "Plain and simple. I don't care if you've got one arm, one leg … no legs. We need you."

"I'll do my best," Mo replied cautiously. "But I don't want to do more damage."

"Worst case, you don't even need to play," Cúper added. "We just need you around the squad – inspire them, give them faith."

Mo had been sceptical. This really felt like his lowest ebb. He'd missed out on the Champions League final, and now there was a good chance that he wouldn't get to play at the World Cup.

He wasn't sure he'd be much fun to be around.

But he was still an optimist at heart. And when he

met up with the squad, he was instantly lifted. They were all so delighted to see him, excited to hear about Liverpool, about breaking the records, asking how his shoulder was.

The last question was the toughest. The doctors and physios had been unsure, and all of them had warned him against playing in the World Cup.

But Mo couldn't miss this opportunity. It was Egypt's first for so long – who knew when they'd be back?

He was on the bench for the first game, and he looked on as they were beaten by a late Uruguay goal. After the game, Mo spoke to Cúper.

"Start me in the next one," he said, firmly. "Just start me."

"Are you sure?" the manager asked. "What have the doctors said?"

"It doesn't matter," Mo insisted. "I'm good to play. I know the risks – I want to play. I *have* to."

"If you know what you're doing," Cúper shrugged. "We could do with you."

The next game had been just as bad, even with Mo on the pitch. He'd had a few flashes, skimming a shot wide of the post and launching a couple of mazy runs. Even so, Egypt had gone 3-0 down to hosts Russia.

But then Egypt had won a penalty. And there was only one man who was going to take it.

So here he was, standing 12 yards in front of the Russian keeper. Thousands of Russian fans were behind the goal, jeering and shouting at him.

Egypt hadn't scored in a World Cup since 1990. Even though they were going to lose this game, this would still be a historic moment.

Mo puffed his cheeks and ran forward. He knew where he was going to put the ball and he blasted it high into the top corner, way out of the reach of the keeper.

GOAL!

Mo pumped his fists as he was grabbed by his team-mates. It was a huge moment for them – and for the millions watching at home in Egypt. An Egyptian had scored a World Cup goal.

Even injured, Mo was breaking records.

17
REDEMPTION

June 2019, Wanda Metropolitano Stadium, Madrid, Spain
Champions League Final, Liverpool v Tottenham Hotspur

"We've got two aims this season," Jürgen Klopp told his team during the first meeting of the new season. He held up two fingers. "One, the Premier League – and two, the Champions League."

"You reckon we can do that?" Sadio Mané whispered to Mo.

"We ended up a long way off Man City in the league,

but we beat them three times last year," Mo replied. "We can do anything."

Since losing to Real Madrid in the Champions League final a year ago, it had been all change at the club.

Fabinho, Alisson and Naby Keïta had all arrived for significant transfer fees, bolstering a squad that already included Virgil van Dijk, Sadio Mané, Jordan Henderson and Roberto Firmino.

And Mo. Mo was top of the list, the record-breaking goalscorer and one of the best players in the world.

A whole host of awards had come Mo's way at the end of 2018. He'd come third in the Best FIFA Men's Player awards, he'd won African Footballer of the Year for the second year in a row – and the Puskás Award, given to the best goal of the year, for his strike against Everton.

By January, Liverpool were top of the league and unbeaten, although Man City were close on their tail, hunting them down.

Mo hadn't quite replicated his unprecedented form from the previous year, but he was still the club's top scorer. He was still the one the other players looked to to get the goals.

After a 2-1 defeat to Man City early in January, Liverpool's first and only defeat in the league, followed by a couple of disappointing draws, the season turned. Now it was City who had the advantage, and Liverpool were the hunters, desperately in pursuit of their title rivals.

Ultimately, it wouldn't be enough. Liverpool finished the season with a record 97 points, but they were still a point behind City, who retained their Premier League title.

"Any other season and we'd have won," Fabinho said to Mo, with a shake of his head. After the final league game of the season, the players were walking around Anfield, applauding the fans.

"It doesn't matter any more," Mo replied. "It's in the past now. We'll be back next season."

Yet he couldn't avoid thinking about all the misses he'd had during the season. They had been so close.

Perhaps, if he'd found the net with that shot, or passed there and set someone up … or …

Mo could only imagine what might have been.

At the highest levels of professional football, the margin for error was so small. But, this season, it had been narrower than ever before.

"Lads! We turn our attention to next week," Klopp reminded them. "Don't let this bring you down. We have another final to win."

He was right. Liverpool hadn't won the league, but after an outstanding European campaign, including a dramatic comeback win at Anfield against Barcelona in the semi-finals, Liverpool were back in the Champions League final.

And, in a twist of fate, the final was in Madrid. Now, in the home city of the team that had stopped them a year ago, Liverpool had the opportunity to make amends for that game, to rewrite history.

The team that stood in their way was another English team – Spurs.

"We've already beaten Spurs twice this year, guys," Jordan Henderson said. "We know what they're good at, and we know where they're weak. We take advantage of those weaknesses, we play to our strengths. We've got this."

"They're going to press hard for the first ten, boys," James Milner added. "But so are we. We match them toe-to-toe, and then our fitness will start to show. We're the team in form, we've got the better players. This is our final."

"Last year, we made mistakes," Henderson continued. "But this year is different. We are going to win. Whatever happens, just keep your focus."

Mo was quiet. He wasn't one to do big speeches and get the whole team going. He was focused on his own game, his own personal redemption story. He was going to score today. He could sense it.

It took him just 25 seconds.

Sadio Mané controlled the ball inside the box, and then attempted to flick a cross into the centre. But Moussa Sissoko had stuck out an arm, and the ball cannoned against it.

Mo immediately turned to the ref, joining the rest of the team and the Liverpool fans in the same chorus.

"Handball!"

Without hesitation, the referee pointed at the penalty spot. Mo was the penalty-taker for the Liverpool team. This was his chance.

He'd hit quite a few different pens in his time. He knew what the options were.

Placing them carefully and sending the keeper the wrong way, or powerful shots into the top corner. Occasionally, in training, he'd even gone for the Panenka, chipping the ball down the middle.

But this was no time to take risks. This was the Champions League final.

Mo took several steps back, pacing his way to the edge of the area. He had only one thing on his mind.

He ignored the words from his team-mates, the shouts from both sets of fans, the taunts and comments from the opposition. This was just about him and the ball.

The referee blew his whistle. Mo breathed out slowly and charged forward, striking the ball hard with his left boot, blasting it at the middle of the goal.

It wasn't his best penalty and it wasn't his most accurate, or the cleanest. But it was hard.

As Hugo Lloris flung himself to his left, the ball sailed past him into the middle of the goal.

GOAL!

Mo had scored in Madrid, and Liverpool were 1-0 up in the Champions League final.

"This doesn't change anything!" Jordan Henderson bellowed, grabbing his team-mates in celebration. "We need to score again. We keep this intensity!"

As it happened, the penalty was the most eventful thing that happened during the first half. The game was cagey and scrappy, with both teams struggling to get any possession.

The second half was much the same, and any chances that came Mo's way were blocked, or he was crowded out as he tried to weave his way through the Spurs defence.

It took until the 86th minute for Liverpool to get their second goal, when Divock Origi blasted the ball into the back of the net.

Liverpool had done it. Mo was a European Champion.

He'd won the trophy that he'd grown up seeing his idols get nowhere near. The Brazilian Ronaldo had never won it. Totti had never won it. But now, Mo had.

And he'd scored in the final.

If it was nothing else, it was redemption for losing one year ago.

18
A LONG WAIT

The Champions League had been Mo's dream. The Premier League was Liverpool's.

The club had come within a whisker of winning it the previous year, with City beating them by a single point.

Mo had seen the images of John Stones' clearance at the Etihad, the millimetres that had separated Liverpool from their first Premier League title.

The aim for the new year had been to establish a team that could compete with City's all-conquering side and win the Premier League title.

In fact, Liverpool did more than just compete. They won 26 of their first 27 games and drew the other game, putting them a mammoth 22 points clear at the top. They also equalled City's record of 18 consecutive Premier League wins.

Mo was still setting his own records as well. On his 100th league appearance for the club, he added his 70th goal, breaking the record of Fernando Torres, who had scored "just" 63 in his first 100 league appearances.

Mo had also become the first Liverpool player since 2003 to score at least 20 goals in three consecutive seasons.

But it wasn't just the Premier League trophy that Liverpool were after. Their success in the Champions League meant that they were involved in the European Super Cup and the Club World Cup – and they won both.

It was yet more silverware to add to Mo's growing collection.

In March, Liverpool finally lost a league game, a 3-0 defeat at Watford, although they remained over 20 points clear at the top of the table. It was quickly becoming a matter of when, rather than if, they would lift the title.

Even a three-month break in the season, due to the coronavirus pandemic, couldn't stop them.

The first game for Mo after the break was at Anfield, against Crystal Palace. There was an eerie atmosphere around the stadium, as the ground that was normally filled with noise and the chants and cheers of thousands of fans was silent.

"It's weird, alright," Trent Alexander-Arnold remarked, as they warmed up before the game.

"It feels like we shouldn't be here," Mo commented.

The game was important for Liverpool. They were just five points from sealing their first-ever league title and, although they couldn't secure the title today, they could get within one match of winning it.

If Liverpool could clinch the league, it would be the earliest a team had ever won the title in terms of matches played, but, because of delays in the season owing to COVID, it would also be the latest. Such was the topsy-turvy world of pandemic football.

"We know what we have to do here tonight," Klopp insisted. "It doesn't matter that there's nobody here. There's going to be millions watching at home, urging us on. They'll expect us to do the business here."

"We're five points from history, boys," Henderson added. "We won't make history tonight, but let's make sure we clinch it as early as possible. I don't want any complacency or anyone relaxing. We need the win."

Mo nodded. He'd won league titles before, with Basel in Switzerland, and he had been part of Chelsea's title-winning squad, even if he hadn't really felt like it at the time.

But this was different. This was an opportunity to be a part of history – the first Liverpool team to win the Premier League. He wasn't going to let it happen quietly.

Liverpool started relentlessly, with Roberto Firmino, Georginio Wijnaldum and Jordan Henderson all going close. It didn't take long for the first goal to come, when Trent Alexander-Arnold whipped home a free kick.

Liverpool now had the advantage, but Mo was determined that the game wouldn't end without his name on the scoresheet.

Fabinho picked the ball up deep, and Mo was instantly on the run.

"Fab! Now!" he shouted, gesturing in behind with his arm.

The ball was deftly lifted over the top and Mo sprinted after it. He got there first, holding off the defender and charging his way into the box.

As the keeper came out, Mo dinked the ball lightly over him and watched it roll into the back of the net.

2-0! Surely Liverpool were going to be champions?

They added two more in the second half, a thunderbolt from Fabinho and another from Sadio Mané.

As the players left the pitch at the end of the match, Mo pictured the millions watching on TV – the fans who had waited 30 years to see Liverpool win a Premier League title, the fans who had supported them through thick and thin, and had cheered them on.

Liverpool might not have won the title today, but

they'd made a huge step in the right direction. They were just two points from winning the league title, two points from another trophy.

As Mo looked at the rest of the team coming off the pitch, he couldn't help but smile.

This wouldn't be the last trophy they won.

19

QUADRUPLE

April 2022, Anfield, Liverpool, England
Liverpool v Manchester United

Quadruple. The word had been whispered around Liverpool before, but never as much as it had been this season. After the chaos of the previous year, Liverpool had seen a complete reversal of their fortunes. They had scraped into the Champions League, after a dramatic end to the season, in which goalkeeper Alisson had scored a header.

The fans had returned to the stadiums, and Liverpool had flourished. Amongst all the ups and downs, Mo continued to score, and he was having one of his best-ever seasons. Top of the goalscoring and assist charts, he was leading the way, with sensational curling strikes against Man City and Watford.

By March, Liverpool had won their first trophy, beating Chelsea in a dramatic penalty shootout in the League Cup.

They were already through to the semi-finals of the Champions League and the final of the FA Cup, and now they were just a point behind Man City in the title race.

But they had been here before. Two years ago, they had been a point behind City in the race for the title – and they'd lost.

If they wanted the quadruple, they would have to do better than that.

"I won't say the word," Klopp told his players, "but we know what we're talking about, what we're after. We know what we're pushing for."

"We've been close before, guys," Milner added. "But

this is the closest we're ever going to get – the closest we're going to get to making history."

"Nobody has ever won all four before," Henderson chimed in. "If we want to be considered the best ever, we have to do that. And if anyone can, it's this squad here."

The next game for Liverpool was at home, against familiar rivals Manchester United. They were playing a day before City's game, so they had an opportunity to put the pressure on and move to the top of the league.

Mo had struggled since returning from the African Cup of Nations in February. Egypt had lost the final on penalties, and, both mentally and physically, Mo had been a shadow of the player who'd started the season in such electric form.

Since then, he had scored four goals in nine league games. For most players, that would be an impressive return, but for Mo it was some of the worst form of his career.

Klopp called him over, before they went out onto the pitch.

"I know you've struggled, Mo," he told him. "But we're going to need you. We're going to need you at your best – and firing. I believe you can get back to it – we all do. If we're going to win these four, we'll need you. So get out there and show everybody what Mo Salah can do."

Mo had a good record against United, having scored a hat-trick against them earlier in the year, as well as a few goals against them in the previous season.

There was a ferocious atmosphere inside the stadium. The players may have been cautious about saying the Q-word, but the fans weren't. They believed it was going to happen.

Liverpool made the perfect start, getting a goal inside five minutes. With United pushing up, they left huge amounts of space behind them, which Liverpool's front-three were more than happy to take advantage of.

Sadio Mané spun a ball over the top and Mo raced after it. He got to the ball first and, seeing the run of Luis Díaz at the far post, he fizzed it across with his right foot.

Díaz was in position to blast it past the keeper and put Liverpool one up.

Mo had got his assist, but he wanted more. He wanted a goal.

After some slick passing play, Sadio Mané flicked the ball over the heads of the United defence. Mo was already on the run, knowing that Sadio would pick him out.

Mo controlled the ball with his right foot, held off the defender and then slid the ball into the back of the net.

GOAL!

He'd scored against United once again.

Mo turned to look at Mané.

"Great ball, Sadio," he grinned. "I needed that."

It was Mané who had scored the winning penalty against Mo's Egypt, only a couple of months ago. Mo was keen to put to bed any rumours that they had fallen out as a result of that. People needed to know that friendship was always more important than rivalry. ,

At half-time Liverpool were still 2-0 up, but then United started to come back. Marcus Rashford went close and Anthony Elanga missed a chance.

But Liverpool weren't going to let them back into this game. They went up another gear and the ball was pulled into the box, for Mané to steer it into the net.

Not long afterwards, Liverpool came forward again, with Diogo Jota sliding a pass into Mo.

Mo held off the defender, saw the onrushing keeper in his eyeline, then got his foot under the ball and lifted it into the air, over the arms of David de Gea.

It was Mo's second goal of the game, Liverpool's fourth and Mo's fifth goal of the season against Man Utd.

It was his 22nd Premier League goal, making it the fifth year in a row that he'd scored over 15 league goals.

It was also a goal that put Liverpool back on top of the Premier League.

Mo soaked in the atmosphere as he celebrated with the fans. He'd come so far since being that skinny little Egyptian kid, struggling to fit in at Basel, the kid who had been cast aside by Chelsea. It was a long way too from the man who had rebuilt his career in Italy.

Now, Mo was one of the best players in the world, with a host of trophies already under his belt. He was one of Liverpool's greatest players, one of the Premier League's best – and, without doubt, Egypt's greatest-ever player.

He had won it all. But now he had his eyes set on making history once more – to be part of the first team ever to win the quadruple.

For many, that would be a distant dream.

But, for Mo Salah, it was just another step on his journey.

HOW MANY
HAVE YOU READ?

MESSI **KANE** **RONALDO** **HAALAND** **SALAH**

PULISIC **LEWANDOWSKI** **MAHREZ** **MBAPPÉ** **SON**

SAKA **SANCHO** **FÉLIX** **GNABRY** **STERLING**

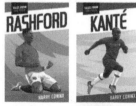   

RASHFORD **KANTÉ** **SILVA** **VAN DIJK**

SOUTHGATE **GUARDIOLA**